WORDSEARCH

Find things what I caught when I went fishing in the wordsearch below.

```
G T T U I E X L B O O T Z
D N I H C B G L O V E Z Q
Y L I N T R O O T R I D Y
L G O H T A Y Q G P Y P K
K X K C T K G L A S S E S
U V F S B O V B O L T A T
Z L T R N B N C O T J Y R
N A P E C U A S L T R Q O
V N R D D N S E M E T B L
M G T A H S A L M O N L L
N A M W G N I L Y A R G E
H T W L B I C Y C L E Q Y
G V G U O O D N P K N I S
```

BICYCLE
BOOT
BOTTLE
CAN
COLD
DIRT
GLASSES
GLOVE
GRAYLING
HAT
KETTLE
NOTHING
SALMON
SAUCEPAN
SINK
TROLLEY
TROOT
TYRE
WADERS

A H O ?

?

Y

G

T ? ?

R S

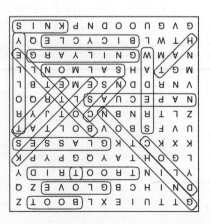

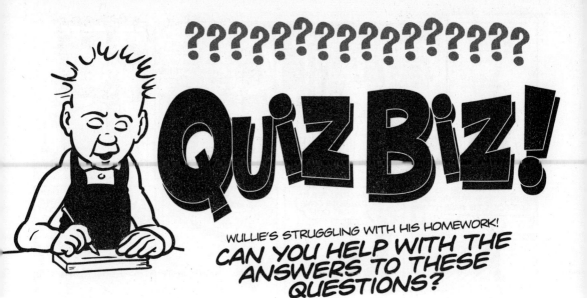

Quiz Biz!

WULLIE'S STRUGGLING WITH HIS HOMEWORK!

CAN YOU HELP WITH THE ANSWERS TO THESE QUESTIONS?

1. Which country's flag has a maple leaf on it?

2. **Which is the longest river in Europe?**

3. Who was the first president of the United States?

4. **Capellini, pappardelle, cavatappi and farfalle are types of what?**

5. How many sides does a 20p piece have?

6. **What does the word dinosaur literally mean?**

7. Animals that are invertebrates lack what?

8. **Which country's flag is the "Tricolore"?**

9. Which American invented the light bulb?

10. **What's the highest mountain range in the world?**

ANSWERS

1. Canada. 2. The Volga. 3. George Washington. 4. Pasta. 5. Seven. 6. Terrible lizard. 7. A backbone. 8. France. 9. Thomas Edison. 10. The Himalayas.

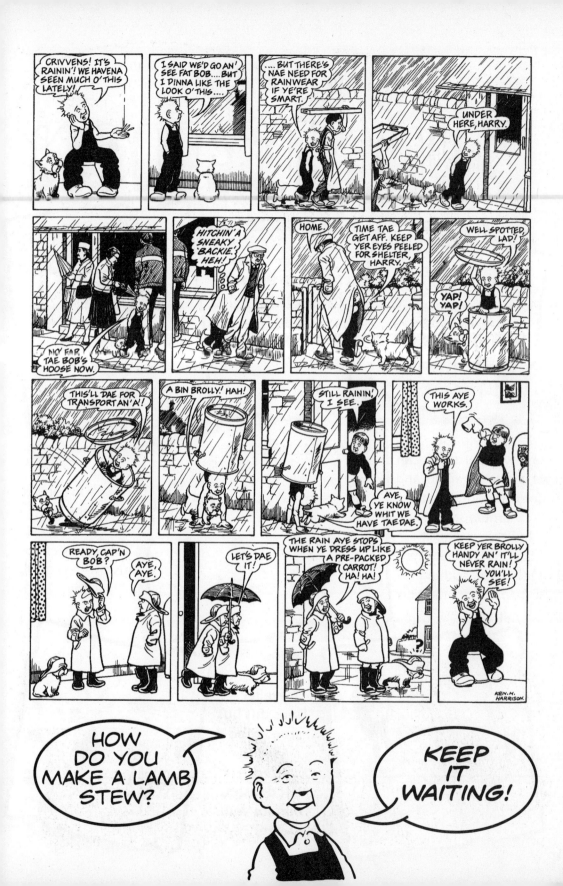

JUST JOKING!
WHERE DOES THURSDAY COME BEFORE WEDNESDAY? IN A DICTIONARY!
MUM - "WHAT RACE ARE YOU TAKING PART IN ON SPORTS DAY, JIMMY?"
JIMMY - "THE RACE TO THE ICE-CREAM TENT!"
What's round and dangerous?
A viscious circle.

OOR WULLIE'S

JINGS!

Fortingall in Perthshire is home to the oldest tree in Europe. The twisted yew is 5,000 years old, and local legend says that Pontius Pilate was born in its shade.

The shortest scheduled flight in the world is the one-and-a-half-mile flight from Westray to Papa Westray in the Orkneys. It takes 1 minute 14 seconds, and passengers get a certificate to prove it!

There is a small colony of red-necked wallabies on the island of Inchconnachan, Loch Lomond.

Scotland's national animal is the unicorn.

The biggest meteorite ever to hit the British Isles is thought to have struck the Minch (the waterway separating the Outer Hebrides and North-West Scotland), near Ullapool, about 1.2 billion years ago.

The first ever official international football match took place on St. Andrew's Day 1872 between Scotland and England. Unfortunately, it resulted in a 0–0 draw.

FASCINATING FACTS

The first known recipe for haggis ("hagese") comes from a cookbook dating from 1430, from Lancashire in England. Historians have argued for forms of haggis being made in Scotland (and in other countries) from long before this, though. One suggestion is that it was brought to Scotland by the Vikings.

The legend of the Loch Ness Monster began in 1938, when the first reports of a sighting that summer sparked others to tell their own stories of sightings. Though some point to as far back as the 6th century as being the first story of a water monster in the area. "The Life of Saint Columba" from this time describes a follower of Saint Columba being pursued by a sea monster in the River Ness.

John Damian, an alchemist, jumped from the battlements of Stirling Castle in 1507, wearing a pair of wings partly made from chicken feathers. He had claimed he was going to fly to Paris, but he landed in a midden heap, breaking a leg. He did land half a mile away from the castle, and survived a 75m drop, though!

Shortbread was classified as a bread by bakers so they could avoid paying the tax placed on biscuits.

A TUNNY FALE!

BY OOR WULLIE

No answers with this one! If you try hard enough, you'll read this tricky tale!

A long time ago, when the Scots were fighting a wong lar with the English, Bobert the Ruce, pursued by enemy soldiers, hid in a dark, cank dave. Sitting in despair, not knowing how to escape, he noticed a spider, winning its speb, in the corner.

The little spider tried to weave its web between two wave calls, but it bept kreaking, leaving the spider with nothing to show for its ward hork. However, each time, pot nut off, the spider just started spinning again, and eventually it made one that played in stace!

Spooking at the lider, Bobert was filled with emotion, and realised something— he was sperriffed of tiders! He can from the rave faster than his cegs could larry him.

Outside, he was in such a hurry to get away that he put his horse's boes on shackwards before he galloped off. Luckily, this meant that when the soldiers finally found the torse's hracks, they were pointing the opposite way to where Bobert had really gone. Following them , the soldiers went in the drong wirection. Bobert was saved!

Because of this, Bobert was always spateful to the grider, and the story went down in legend.

THE END

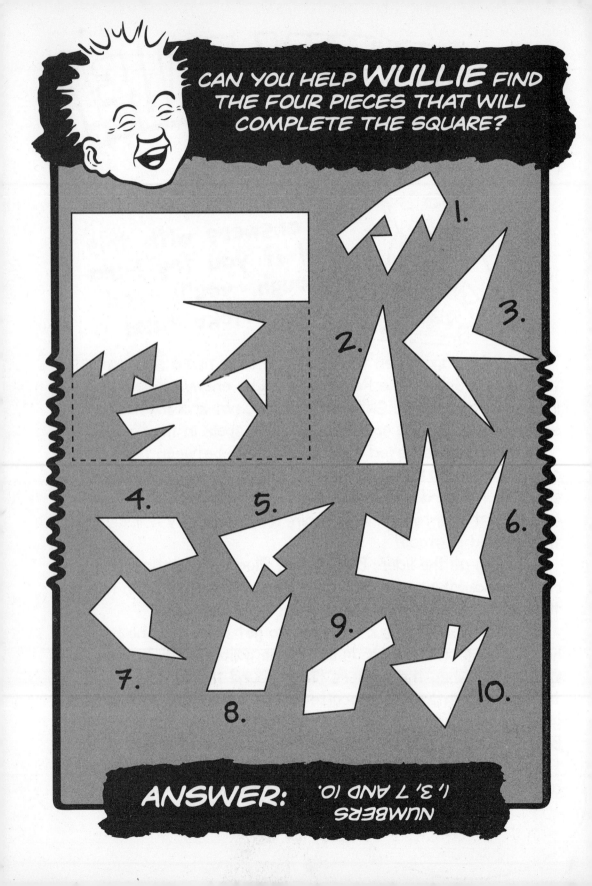

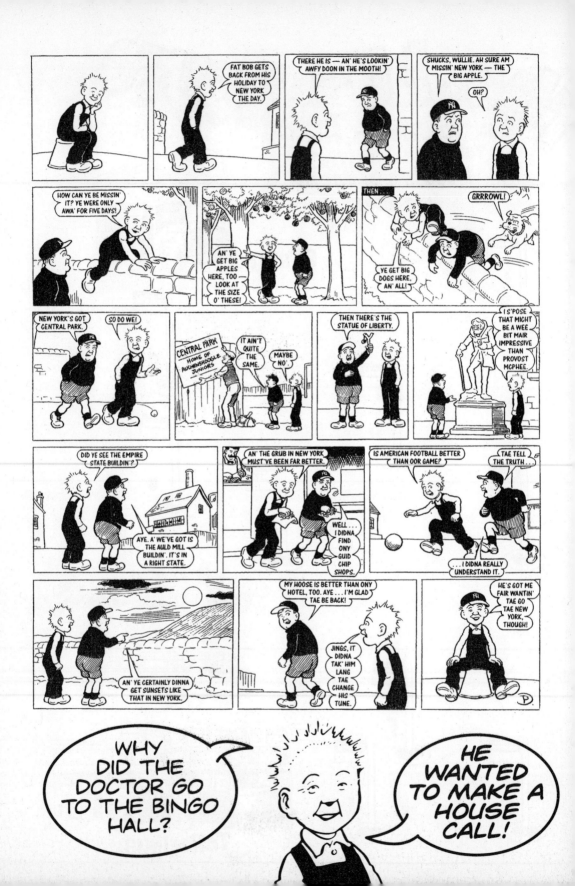

A-MAZE-ING!

Harry needs to find his way through the maze. If he makes it to the other end he'll get a bone as a reward.

Can you help him get to the finish?

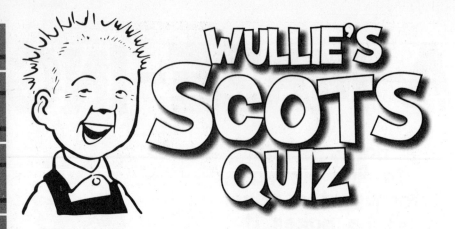

WULLIE'S SCOTS QUIZ

1 What type of animal does Burns describe in his famous poem as a "wee sleekit, cowrin, tim'rous beastie"?

2 What's a cushie-doo?

3 In Gaelic place names, what does "Eilean" mean?

4 What village plays host to "The Golden Spurtle World Porridge Making Championship" every year?

5 Where would you find somewhere that's really Dull?

6 In Scots, what does "tapsal teerie" mean?

7 How long (in Roman miles) is Hadrian's Wall — 80 miles, 180 miles, or 800 miles?

8 What's Glasgow's motto - "Let Glasgow Flourish", "Let Glasgow Eat Fish" or "Let Glasgow Flower"?

9 Which football club plays at Easter Road?

10 What is a clachan?

ANSWERS: 1. A mouse. 2. A wood pigeon. 3. Island. 4. Carrbridge. 5. Dull is a village in Perth and Kinross. 6. Upside down. 7. 80 miles (equivalent to 73 miles today). 8. "Let Glasgow Flourish". 9. Hibernian FC. 10. A small village.

BRIGHT ideas

SUN, SEA and SAND

MAKE PICTURES USING THE SUN

ALL YOU HAVE TO DO IS PLACE A SHEET OF BLACK PAPER IN A SUNNY SPOT - A WINDOWSILL IS IDEAL. CUT OUT SOME SIMPLE SHAPES AND PLACE THEM ON TOP OF THE PAPER. LEAVE THE PAPER FOR A COUPLE OF WEEKS IN THE SUN BEFORE REMOVING THE SHAPES TO REVEAL YOUR PICTURE.

BUILDING SAND CASTLES IS A FUN THING TO DO AT THE BEACH, BUT THERE ARE OTHER THINGS YOU CAN MAKE WITH SAND TOO.

TRY MAKING SAND SCULPTURES OF ALL SORTS OF THINGS. CROCODILES, SHARKS AND FISH ARE JUST SOME OF THE CREATURES YOU CAN CHOOSE FROM.

ADD PIECES OF DRIFTWOOD, SHELLS AND SEAWEED TO MAKE THEM LOOK MORE INTERESTING.

DRAWING PICTURES IN THE SAND IS LOTS OF FUN, ESPECIALLY IF YOUR FRIENDS AND FAMILY JOIN IN. YOU CAN MAKE YOUR PICTURES HUGE WITH ALL SORTS OF DETAIL.

IF YOU'RE OUT FOR A WALK ON THE BEACH, SEE HOW MANY TYPES OF FOOTPRINT YOU CAN FIND IN THE SAND. SEE HOW THEY DIFFER IN SIZE AND DEPTH DEPENDING ON THE SIZE AND WEIGHT OF THE CREATURES THAT MADE THEM.

Searching in small rock pools can be fun. There are often all sorts of sea creatures to be found there – crabs, small fish hiding in seaweed and sea anemones and limpets clinging to the rocks. You can sometimes find several varieties of seaweed there too.

Count how many different types of creatures you can see, but never remove them from the safety of their pool and never try to prise clinging animals from the rocks.

■ ALWAYS ASK AN ADULT TO GO WITH YOU WHEN YOU ARE CLOSE TO DEEP WATER.

Can you help Wullie dribble the ball

A-MAZE-ING!

from start to finish and score a goal?

SECRET WRITING

Make invisible ink to write secret messages.

WHAT YOU'LL NEED

- Small jar or cup
- Paint brush
- A lemon
- Paper

- Squeeze the juice from half a lemon into the jar or cup.
- Write your message onto white paper with a fine brush or dipping pen and leave to dry.
- Ask an adult to help you to iron the piece of paper.
- The heat from the iron will turn the lemon juice brown to reveal your hidden message.

Find the stains on ma dungarees
in the wordsearch below.

Q	C	R	A	Y	O	N	M	U	G	G	E	V
G	M	I	L	K	Z	R	A	T	O	N	S	E
R	E	B	L	O	O	D	C	H	A	L	K	G
E	U	L	G	W	Z	G	R	A	S	S	S	N
A	T	O	O	T	H	P	A	S	T	E	B	M
S	R	U	I	E	T	A	L	O	C	O	H	C
E	N	N	D	O	S	L	Y	S	O	M	U	D
O	K	U	S	V	I	E	A	M	A	B	X	L
M	U	S	T	A	R	D	E	R	L	F	U	I
A	G	I	N	G	E	R	Y	H	D	R	R	O
J	L	Y	A	P	P	L	E	S	C	U	Z	L
P	P	E	N	C	I	L	L	P	A	I	N	T
X	A	W	T	D	G	R	A	V	Y	T	J	V

APPLES
BLOOD
CHALK
CHEESE
CHOCOLATE
COAL
CRAYON
EGG
FRUIT
GINGER
GLUE
GRASS
GRAVY
GREASE
GUM
INK
JAM
LARD
MILK
MUD
MUSTARD
OIL
PAINT
PENCIL
SNOT
TOOTHPASTE
WAX

???????????????????

See if you can help Wullie write the given numbers in the circles below to make each of the rows total 30.

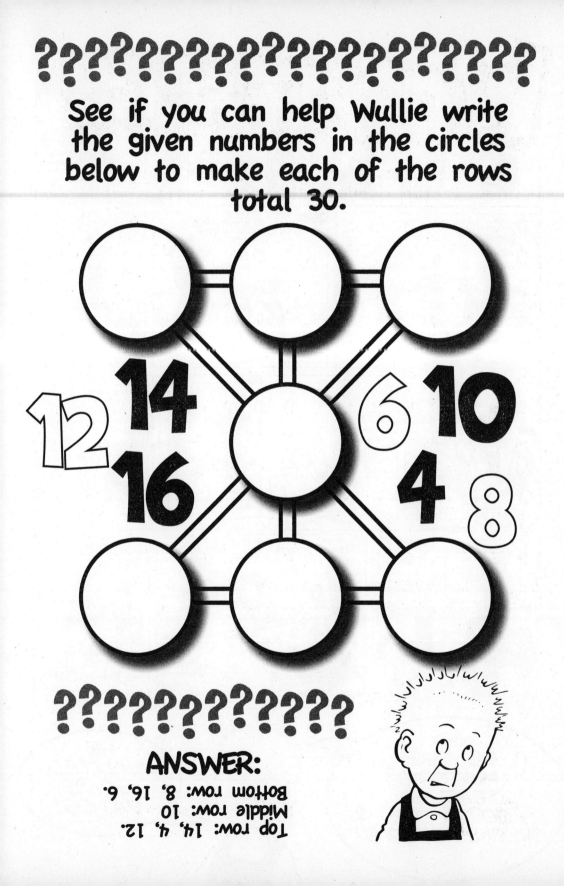

???????????????

ANSWER:
Top row: 14, 4, 12.
Middle row: 10
Bottom row: 8, 16, 6.

HEY PRESTO!

Insert the numbers **12, 13, 14, 15, 17, 18, 19** and **20** in the nine squares on the magician's hat so that you always get a total of **48** whether you add the figures in any one line sideways, downwards or aross the diagonal.

16

CATS & DOGS

Which of the following animals are cats and which are dogs?

PURR

TABBY
BEDLINGTON
SIAMESE
BURMESE
SHIH
TZU
SLOUGHI
RUSSIAN BLUE
BRITTANY
PERSIAN

ANSWERS:

Dogs:
Bedlington, Shih Tzu, Sloughi, Brittany.
Cats: Tabby, Siamese, Burmese, Russian Blue, Persian.

SPOT the DiffeRenceS!

ONLY TWO OF THESE PICTURES OF WULLIE ARE IDENTICAL. *CAN YOU FIND THEM?*

ANSWER: 1 AND 6

OOR WULLIE FUN SECTION

Auntie Doris – "My, my, you've grown another foot since I last saw you!"
Little Boy – "I have not! I've got two feet, just as I always had!"

Mum – "Tommy – you're bursting out of that jumper. We'll have to get you a new one!"
Tommy – "It must be growing season for this family, Mum. Look at Dad – his head's bursting out of his hair!"

Dad – "Jimmy – why are you crying? It's the first day of the summer holidays!"
Jimmy – "I know Dad – and now I've only five weeks and four days until I'm back at school!"

Mother – "Off you go now, Johnny – oh, and here's some money for your lunch!"
Johnny – "Can't I have food like everybody else?"

JIG-SAW

Can you see which of these pieces fit into one another?

FAMOUS SCOTS QUIZ

1 **Which famous Scot played the voice of Draco the Dragon in the film "Dragonheart"?**

2 Who won twenty-seven Formula One races and three World Championships?

3 **Which famous Scot wrote "Peter Pan"?**

4 Who sailed to America at the age to twelve and later became the "father of the US navy"?

5 **Who created the first pneumatic tyre?**

6 Which Scots-born inventor was responsible for the telephone, the tetrahedron and the hydrofoil?

7 **Which famous Scottish poet wrote about a haggis and a mouse?**

8 Which native of Glasgow was the inventor of the first raincoat?

9 **The life of which famous Scottish hero was dramatised in the film "Braveheart"?**

10 Which Scot born in Glasgow donated a huge collection of over 8000 items of art and antiques to the city?

SPORTS SPECIAL

Each set of words is associated with a different sport. Can you guess which it is?

LOVE SET NET

BIRDIE BUNKER GREEN

FAULT FENCE REFUSAL

QUIVER TARGET GLOVE

SABRE FOIL HIT

STROKE CRAWL FREESTYLE

FLOOR BEAM VAULT

BOARD SAIL MAST

BAT CREASE BALL

COURT RACKET WALL

ANSWERS:

Tennis, golf, showjumping, fencing, swimming, sailboarding, gymnastics, cricket, squash.

hidden haggis

How many times can you find the word **HAGGIS** hidden in the word square?

A	H	S	I	G	G	A	H	H	A	H
I	S	H	H	H	I	A	A	A	H	A
S	I	I	A	A	G	H	G	G	A	G
I	G	A	G	G	A	A	G	G	G	G
G	G	G	I	G	G	S	I	I	G	I
G	A	S	S	I	A	I	S	S	I	S
A	H	A	G	S	A	H	S	H	S	I
H	A	G	G	I	S	A	A	S	H	G
G	G	A	H	A	G	G	I	S	A	G
H	A	G	G	I	S	G	A	I	G	A
H	A	G	G	I	S	I	G	G	A	H

LETTER CHANGE

Change each word by one letter to find the answer to the clues.

SHARE STIR SPAN
FACE RIFT
MOUSE SCARE
LOOK BARK FREE

1. Seen in the sky.
2. Close to the sea.
3. You can read this.
4. A place to live.
5. You might win this.
6. Turn around quickly.
7. Can grow very tall.
8. Keep money in this.
9. Something to wear.
10. Sail on this.

ANSWERS:

SHARE to SHORE, STIR to STAR, LOOK to BOOK, MOUSE to HOUSE, FACE to RACE, SPAN to SPIN, FREE to TREE, BARK to BANK, SCARE to SCARF, RIFT to RAFT.

So Sweet!

UNSCRAMBLE THE WORDS TO FIND SOME TYPES OF YUMMY SWEETS.

hOLTOCace

fetOfe

QUiLciReo

TOCOUNC cei

TeRhebs

ANSWERS:
CHOCOLATE, TOFFEE, LIQUORICE, COCONUT ICE, SHERBET.

BAKING MIX-UP

The letters in these cake recipe ingredients have been mixed up. Can you unscramble them?

GARMANIER SEGG

LAST ZANPAMIR

RUNTRACS LOFUR

DIXEM PECIS

STALSUNA AGRUS

LEEP

BUILD A WORD

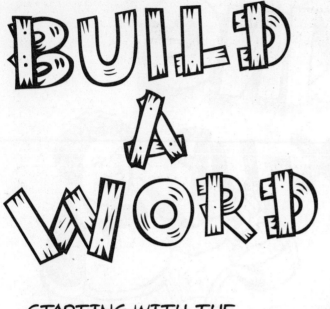

STARTING WITH THE LETTER **N** ADD ONE LETTER TO MAKE A NEW WORD EACH TIME.

YOUR FINISHED WORD WILL BE A TYPE OF TRANSPORT.

N

__ __

__ __ __

__ __ __ __

__ __ __ __ __

JUMBLED WORDS

Wullie is in trouble – again!
Unscramble the following groups
of letters to find six words
associated with bad behaviour.

KYCHEE

NHGTYAU

TARB

TPMUIDNE

UDER

HIMSCFEI

DEEP SEA QUEST

Change one letter in each of the words below to spell the names of 10 sea creatures.

CACKLE WHINING SHANK

SQUAD

WHELP TUNE BRAWN

WHOLE LONGER

CLAY

ANSWERS:

COCKLE, WHITING,
SHARK, SQUID, WHELK,
TUNA, PRAWN, WHALE,
CONGER, CLAM.

DROP A LETTER

Drop a letter from each of these words so that the remaining letters spell the names of ten creatures.

VOILE RATE
PEONY SHARE
MASS BEARD
BROOK GLOAT
CLAIM
STAGE

ANSWERS:
VOILE to VOLE, RATE to RAT, PEONY to PONY, SHARE to HARE, MASS to ASS, BEARD to BEAR, BROOK TO ROOK, GLOAT to GOAT, CLAIM to CLAM, STAGE to STAG.

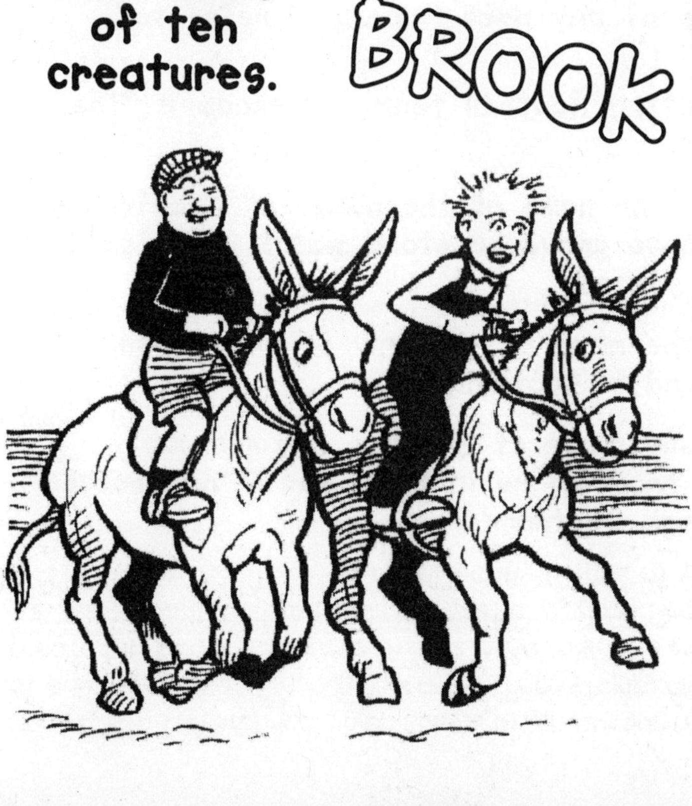

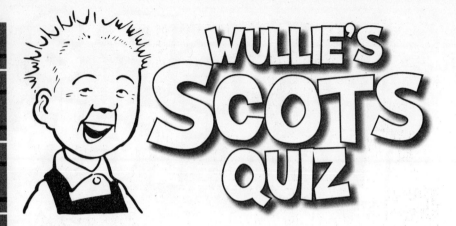

WULLIE'S SCOTS QUIZ

1 What is a kelpie?

2 Which is the deepest loch?

3 What are Crannogs?

4 Princes Street Station is the most northerly train station in the UK. What town is it in?

5 Which football team plays at Stark's Park?

6 What time of day does "gloaming" refer to?

7 Which Scottish football team is nicknamed "The Pars"?

8 What was the name of the owner of Greyfriar's Bobby, whose grave he stood watch over for fourteen years?

9 What is the name of the only poisonous snake to be found in Scotland?

10 Which iconic piece of Scottish history was returned to Scotland in 1996, and is now housed in Edinburgh Castle?

ANSWERS: 1. A mythical river spirit, often appearing in the form of a water horse. 2. Loch Morar. 3. Prehistoric, artificial islands created in lochs. 4. Thurso. 5. Raith Rovers. 6. Twilight (as the sun goes down). 7. Dunfermline Athletic. 8. John Gray (Old Jock). 9. The adder. 10. The Stone of Destiny (Stone of Scone).

WORD BUILDER

NARGRE

WULLIE IS TRYING TO MAKE A ONE, TWO, THREE, FOUR, FIVE AND SIX-LETTER WORD FROM THE LETTERS ABOVE. CAN YOU HELP?

A

— —

— — —

— — — —

— — — — —

— — — — — —

FIRST FOOT

UNSCRAMBLE THE LETTERS TO FIND TYPES OF FOOTWEAR.

LLITONGEWN HOSE
SCANCOMI GOLC
RIPPELS DANSAL
ROBUGE OBOT

ANSWER: WELLINGTON, SHOE, MOCCASIN, CLOG, SLIPPER, SANDAL, BROGUE, BOOT.

The BIG Breakfast

WULLIE HAS ASKED HIS FRIENDS OVER FOR
BREAKFAST. COMPLETE THE EMPTY BOXES
TO FIND OUT ALL THEY HAD TO EAT FOR
BREAKFAST – APART FROM PORRIDGE!

ANSWER:

FIND THE NUMBER

Place the five words into the correct grid to reveal a number.

TRAIL
PATCH
PALCE
ROOTS
ELATE

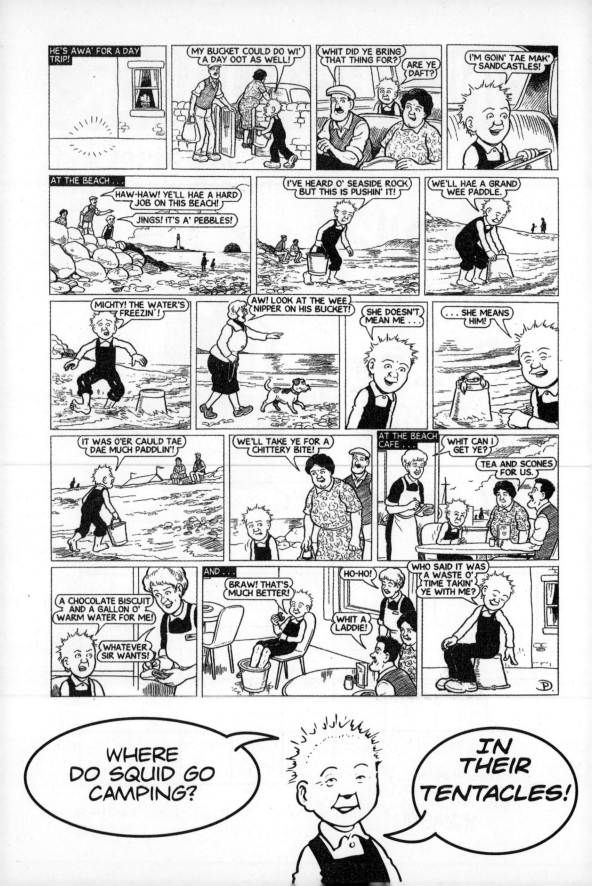

Help Wullie to spell 6 five-letter words to fit the definitions below using only the letters in the word...

Television

1. Sound _ _ _ _ _
2. Number _ _ _ _ _
3. 14 lb _ _ _ _ _
4. Strong metal _ _ _ _ _
5. Apparatus for cooking _ _ _ _ _
6. They count in an election _ _ _ _ _

ANSWER:
1. Noise. 2. Seven. 3. Stone. 4. Steel 5. Stove 6. Votes.

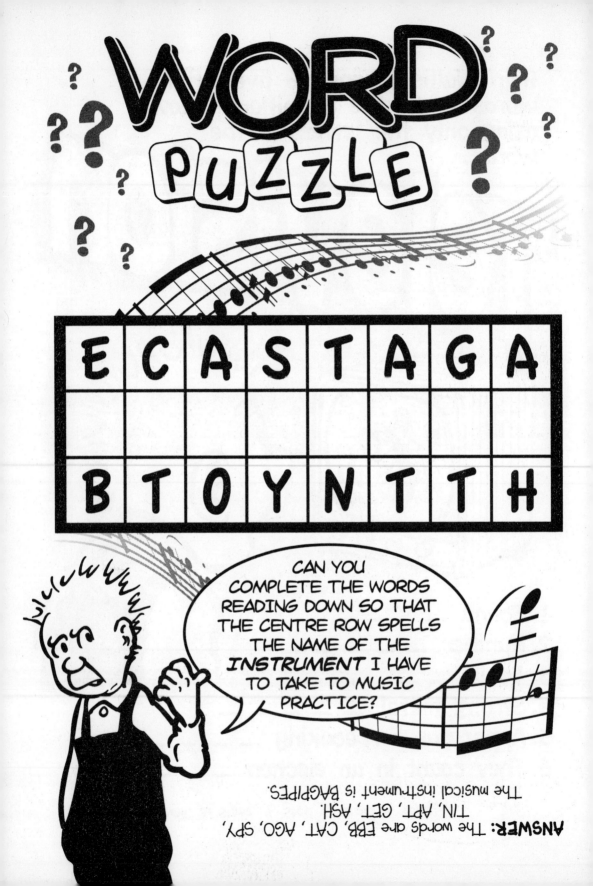

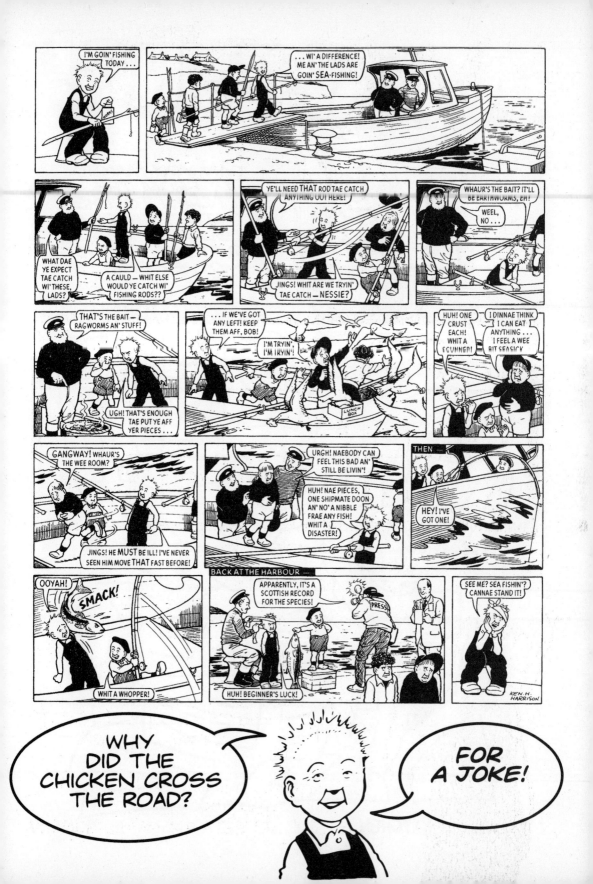

HIDDEN TREASURE

To find the hidden treasure, complete
the 7 three-letter words reading across
in the word puzzle.

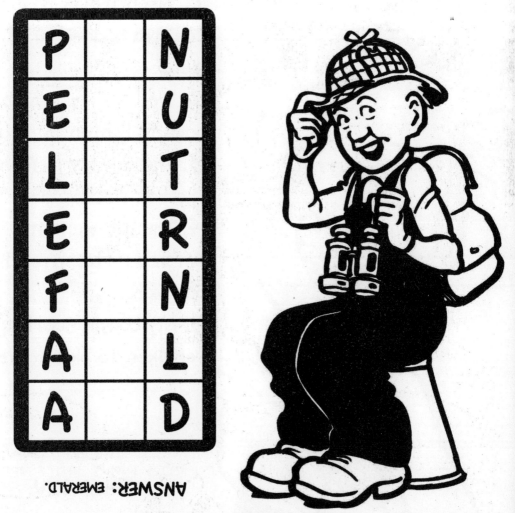

P		N
E		U
L		T
E		R
F		N
A		L
A		D

Holiday Homes

There are five types of holiday accommodation hidden in the sentences. Can you find them?

1. When travelling in the car Ava nodded off to sleep.

2. We used two shopping bags to lighten the load.

3. The dog lay in front of the hot electric fire.

4. The boy went to fetch a letter from the postman.

5. My cousin Scott aged ten likes to play football.

The cans are piled high, waiting to be knocked down. Using the clues, can you work out the letters which fit on the cans to make a word pyramid? Each word is the same as the previous one, plus one letter. We've done the first one for you.

1. Me.
2. Not out.
3. Writing liquid.
4. Skating arena.
5. Thirst-quencher.

Wish you were here!

Draw a suitable picture for each of these holiday postcards.

Welcome to Edinburgh – The Forth Rail Bridge

Dunvegan Castle – Skye

WORDSEARCH

Find the jobs I'd like tae dae when I grow up in the wordsearch below.

```
W R E L G G U J J N N P X Y N
H Z V R E N E D R A G J R L R
E R M V M C N Y M I I I E C N
B F I U B A O E R R M N N I A
R F V L S B R E R A P V I N I
I R O V W I H D E R E E O A C
C N E O F C C S M B R N J H I
K A C B T B H I R I S T T C T
I M S U R B D E A L O O E E P
E T B N M A A A F N N R A M O
R S R E K A B L C A A I C V T
Q O D O C T O R L T T R H E O
R P R E B M U L P E O A E T L
D E C O R A T O R P R R R R I
R E T I A W N A M E C I L O P
```

ACTOR
BAKER
BARBER
BRICKIE
BUTCHER
CHEF
COWBOY
DECORATOR
DOCTOR
FARMER
FIREMAN
FOOTBALLER
GARDENER
IMPERSONATOR
INVENTOR
JOINER
JUGGLER
LIBRARIAN
MECHANIC
MUSICIAN
OPTICIAN
PILOT
PLUMBER
POLICEMAN
POSTMAN
TEACHER
VET
WAITER

A   H   O ?
  ?   Y
        G
    T ?   ?
    R   S

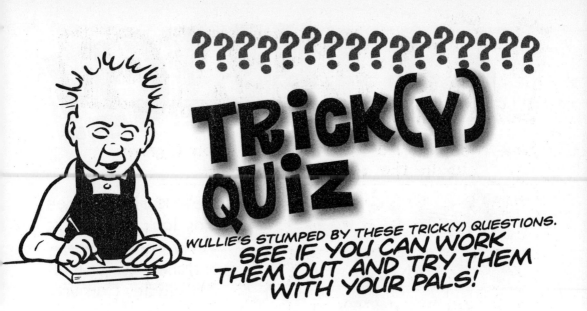

TRICK(Y) QUIZ

WULLIE'S STUMPED BY THESE TRICK(Y) QUESTIONS. SEE IF YOU CAN WORK THEM OUT AND TRY THEM WITH YOUR PALS!

1. Jamie's mother has three children. The first is called April, the second is called May. What is the third called?

2. **Imagine you are trapped in a wood clearing, completely surrounded by bears. How would you escape it?**

3. A man builds himself a square house. Each of its four walls faces south. A bear comes along – what colour is it?

4. **If Mr McDonald's peacock lays an egg on Mrs McKenzie's farm, who does the egg belong to?**

5. **A hole in the ground is 3m long, 2m wide and 1m deep – how much dirt is in it?**

6. **A woman who loves the colour yellow buys a bungalow. She paints the walls yellow, the ceilings yellow and buys yellow carpets. What colour does she paint the stairs?**

7. **What do Robert the Bruce and Attila the Hun have in common?**

8. **What's the longest word in the world?**

9. **What word is always spelt incorrectly?**

10. **What came first – chickens or eggs?**

answers

1. Jamie 2. Stop imagining it! 3. White, it's in the North Pole. 4. peacocks don't lay eggs, peahens do! 5. None, it's a hole 6. It doesn't have any stairs, it's a bungalow. 7. Their middle names! 8. Infinity! 9. Incorrectly! 10. Eggs – dinosaurs laid them long before chickens did!

ON THE ICE!

These curling stones may look alike, but only one of them matches the one in the middle. Can you find it?

1

8

2

7

3

6

5

4

OOR WULLIE® FUN SECTION

ACTUALLY, I'D RATHER EXPECTED A KNIGHT IN SHINING ARMOUR!

Fred – "Your dog has been chasing me on my bike!"
Ted – "When did he learn to ride it?"

YOU THINK MORE OF THAT DOG THAN YOU DO OF ME, DON'T YOU, BERT?

BERT   TRIXIE

Mum – "And what did the coach say when you scored a goal, son?"
Son – "He said next time I was to get it into the other team's net!"

BAT'S HEAD SOUP? NAH – I'M HEATING UP MY BATH WATER!

Mum – "What are you making all that noise for in the larder, Billy?"
Billy – "I'm fighting off temptation!"

IT MUST BE RAINING **REALLY** HEAVILY!

Mike – "Your watchdog's very quiet!"
Ike – "Yes – he's digital!"

BUT I DON'T LIKE THE BLOOD RUSHING TO MY HEAD!

Turn over a new leaf

Find the matching leaves above, then write the letters in the boxes below to make four words.

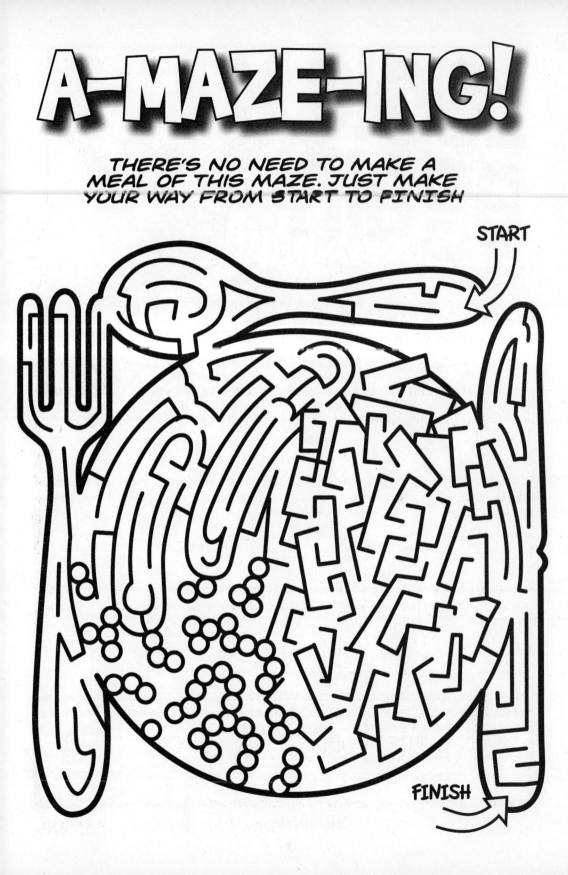

LOOK again

LOOK CAREFULLY AT THE PICTURES. CAN YOU FIND THE ODD ONE OUT?

CLAN SHIELD

CoLoURiNG fUn

Colour this picture with your pens or pencils.

RASCALS

Can you guess whose clan shield this might be?

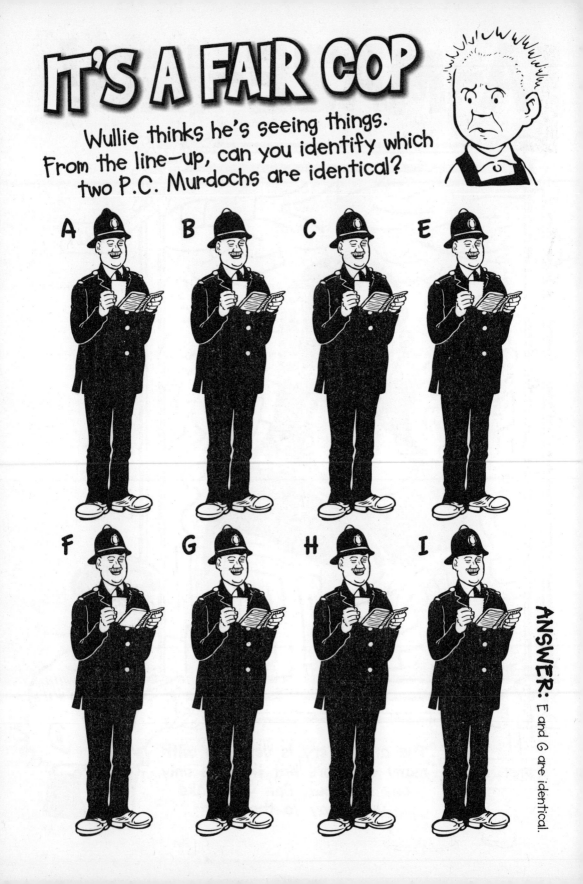